Color Theory

It helps to understand some color theory when planning a color scheme. There are three primary colors: yellow, red, and blue. You cannot make them from mixing other colors. If you mix two primary colors together, you get a secondary color (for example, yellow and red make orange). If you mix a secondary color with a primary color, you get a tertiary color.

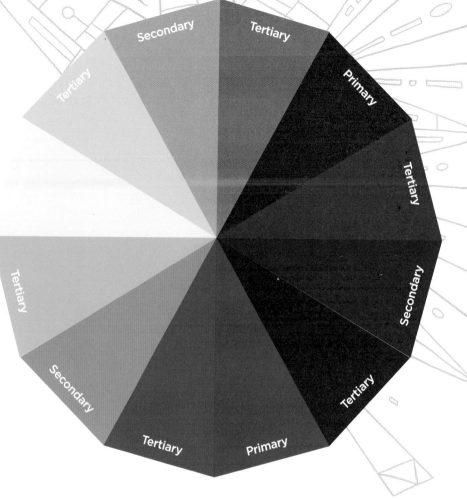

Complementary colors are opposite each other on the color wheel and provide strong contrast.

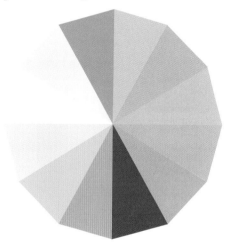

Analogous colors are next to each other on the color wheel and have a cohesive effect.

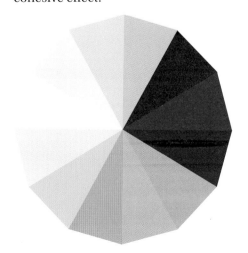

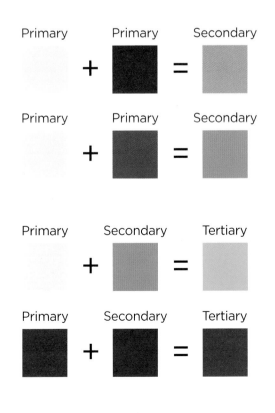

Primary	Primary	Secondary
	+	=

Primary	Primary	Secondary
	+	=

Primary	Secondary	Tertiary
	+	=

Primary	Secondary	Tertiary
	+	=

How to Bible Journal with This Book

This coloring book is meant to be both fun and reflective, allowing you to engage with the ideas expressed in the art, but you can also take that activity outside of this book! Bible journaling, a faith-based trend that is steadily growing in popularity, is the act of journaling and drawing in the margins of your Bible or in a separate journal in order to connect with and reflect on your faith. This book provides you with three pages of art (at the end of the book) that is custom-made for use in Bible journaling—including useful items like bookmarks, tags, borders, and more. But you can also use any art from the entire book—you aren't limited to those three pages! And you have a lot of options for what to do with the art you decide to use:

CUT IT OUT. Super simple: just color a design, cut it out, and glue it into your Bible!

TRACE IT. If you want to reuse a design more than once, trace it directly into your Bible.

COPY IT. Try photocopying a design onto colored paper or a piece of vellum.

Cut out and color a bookmark to save your place.

Trace a design on vellum and attach it with washi tape.

Color and label a page flag.

How to Enhance Your Coloring

Doing more than just filling in areas with solid color can be one of the most enjoyable parts of coloring! Follow along as I color and embellish this piece in a variety of ways.

Fill the sections. In this piece, I started by filling all the main shapes with marker.

Add a halo. I used marker to add a colored "halo" that surrounds all the leaves and flowers in order to give those elements a background that groups them together.

Add details. I used a single deep shade of teal colored pencil to add more details and patterns within the large teal letters. Using a darker shade of the same color helps keep the section cohesive.

Add shading and doodles. I used colored pencil shading to create dimension on the bird. I also added whimsical lacy doodles around the heart and leaves with a pen.

Add some pops of white. To finish this piece, I used white gel pen to add highlight dots to the heart, some flowers, and the dot of the "i" in "Rejoice." Gel pen is great because it sits on top of a colored image almost like paint.

Color Stories

What colors does your love bloom in? Soft and romantic, or lively and bold? Color sets the mood and emotion in our images and is so fun to play with! These examples feature the same image colored in different ways to show the variety of feelings you can get from unique color stories.

Deep and earthy red and orange colors are warm and full of energy. I think of fall leaves changing color in vibrant oranges. To keep this combination from having too much red, I used a khaki color in the surround around my little leaves. The slight hint of green mixed within that color complements the reds. Purple accents in the berries and flower centers add a touch of royalty. The light yellow of LOVE almost jumps off the page when placed on top of these deep and rich colors.

Springtime LOVE blooms with fresh green vines and romantic pink and orange flowers. I've used a mix of greens here to show variety in the garden. My surround on the leaves is a chartreuse with the warmth of yellow added to the green, which nicely mixes with the more aqua shade of the larger leaf sides. Pink and orange flowers give playful pops of warm color nestled in the greenery. The outline of LOVE is a deeper red shade to separate it from the background while the lighter interior is a romantic pink.

The blue LOVE feels serene and calm in a cooler palette. The flowers bring in a little warmth by mixing red with blue to get purple petals and by having warm centers. I decided to use muted shades of the warm colors to complement the cool tones of the blues and purples. The background is lighter here, with LOVE being a contrasting element on top.

The teal LOVE is rich and colorful with an eclectic, global feel. Teal can look cool or warm based on what colors it is paired with. The gold and orange tones are tertiary complements that work well with medium and deep pink accent colors against the teal. Just as in the deep red LOVE image, I've used color throughout the background. I've mimicked the small leaf shapes to make my background edges.

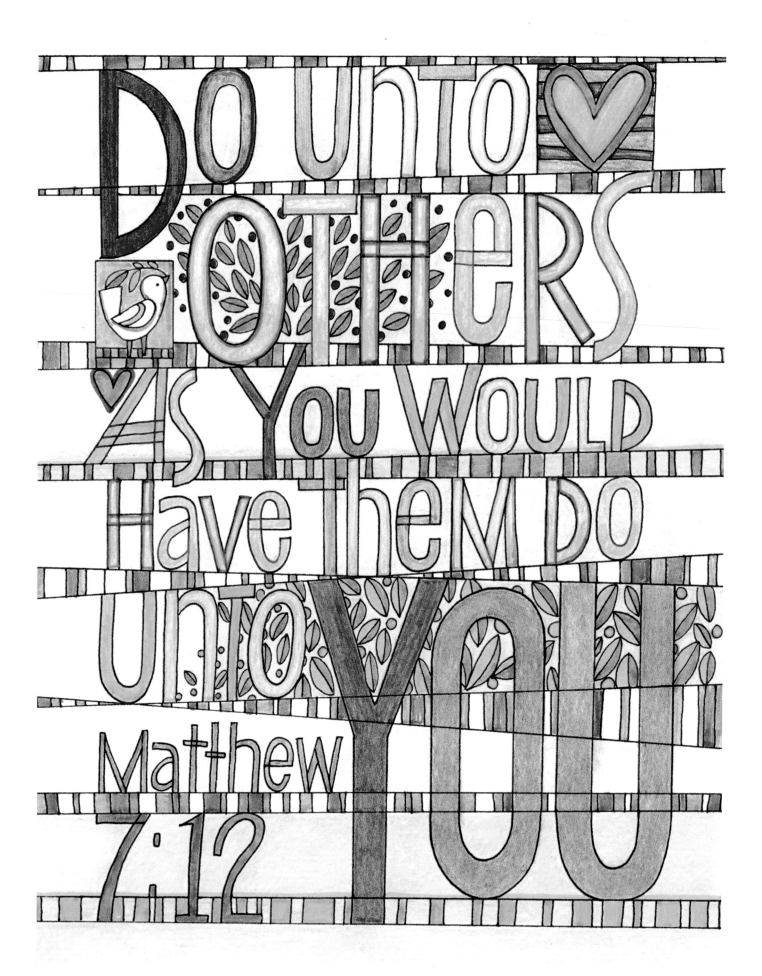

Do unto others as you would have them do unto you. Matthew 7:12

Markers (Crayola), colored pencils (Prismacolor). Color by Darla Tjelmeland.   Matthew 7:12, page 65.

find Strength in
faith &
family

Colored pencils (Faber-Castell). Color by Lynette Parmenter.

Faith and Family, page 37.   7

whatever one sows,

GALATIANS 6:7

that will he also reap

Markers (Sharpie), colored pencils. Color by Roslyn Coronado.

He has made everything beautiful in its time.

Ecclesiastes 3:11

Let all that you do be done in

LOVe

that done

Markers (Tombow, Blick), colored pencils (Prismacolor). Color by Robin Pickens.

Be
JOYFUL
in hope,

PATIENT
in affliction,

FAITHFUL
in prayer.

ROMANS 12:12

don't be afraid, just believe

Mark 5:36

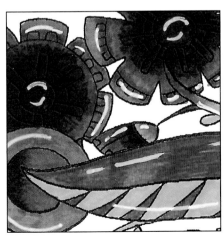

Pens (Staedtler), colored pencils (Prismacolor), markers (Sharpie), gel pens (Uni-Ball Signo). Color by Keara Irby.

with God all things are possible.

MATTHEW 19:26

Colored pencils (Faber-Castell, Prismacolor). Color by Lynette Parmenter.

Matthew 19:26, page 23.

GOD is Within Her She Will Not Fall

Psalm 46:5

Markers (Copic, Spectrum Noir), colored pencils (Prismacolor). Color by Lisa Caryl.

start each day with a

grateful

heart

Markers (Tombow, Blick), colored pencils (Prismacolor). Color by Robin Pickens. Grateful Heart, page 47.

FOR EVERYONE WHO ASKS RECEIVES,

AND THE ONE WHO SEEKS FINDS,

AND TO THE ONE WHO KNOCKS, THE DOOR WILL BE OPENED.

MATTHEW 7:8

How would the world be impossible to live in
if God granted every prayer request?

Matthew 7:8

Be
JOYFUL
in hope,
PATIENT
in affliction,
FAITHFUL
in prayer.

ROMANS 12:12

Why is this verse a blueprint for
dealing with difficult circumstances?

Romans 12:12

THE PATH OF THE RIGHTEOUS IS LIKE THE MORNING SUN.
SHINING EVER BRIGHTER LIKE THE FULL LIGHT OF DAY.

PROVERBS 4:18

Why is the path of the righteous
compared to the light of day in this verse?
What makes this comparison feel true?

Proverbs 4:18

with God
all things
are possible.

MATTHEW 19:26

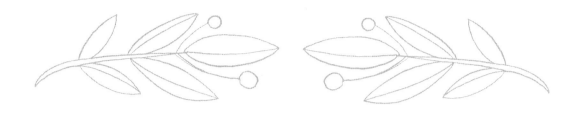

Reflect on a time in your life
when you witnessed God taking control.

Matthew 19:26

For God so loved the world...

John 3:16

What sacrifices have you made for a loved one?
What have loved ones sacrificed for you?

_____
_____
_____
_____
_____
_____
_____

John 3:16

LOVE IS PATIENT
AND KIND;
LOVE DOES NOT ENVY
OR BOAST;
IT IS NOT ARROGANT
OR RUDE.
IT DOES NOT INSIST
ON ITS OWN WAY;
IT IS NOT IRRITABLE
OR RESENTFUL;
IT DOES NOT REJOICE
AT WRONGDOING,
BUT REJOICES WITH
THE TRUTH.
LOVE BEARS ALL THINGS,
BELIEVES ALL THINGS,
HOPES ALL THINGS,
ENDURES ALL THINGS.

1 CORINTHIANS 13:4-7

This verse is the definition of how to love.
Which parts do you struggle with?

1 Corinthians 13:4-7

AS FOR ME AND MY HOUSE, WE WILL SERVE the LORD.

JOSHUA 24:15

List some concrete ways
that you personally can serve God.

_____

_____

_____

_____

_____

_____

_____

Joshua 24:15

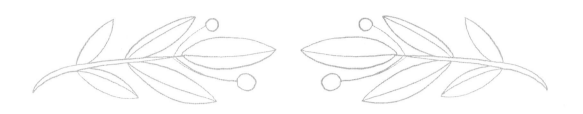

Think of someone in your life who needs your forgiveness.
How can you begin to forgive them?

Compassion Gives You Wings

By using green for "grace" and nothing else, it's clear what the main message of this piece is.

How do you define "grace" in the religious sense?

Grace

Let all that you do be done in LOVE

1 Corinthians 16:14

The warm colors of the border's hearts are repeated in the word "love" for a charming, cohesive look.

Think of your everyday activities.
Which of them do you need
to start doing in love?

In Love

find Strength in

faith &

family

Blending the vivid red to the glowing yellow in
the leaves creates a beautiful ombré effect.

How does your family give you strength?

Faith and Family

The bright blue of these letters might have seemed out of place if the same blue hadn't also been used in the floral details.

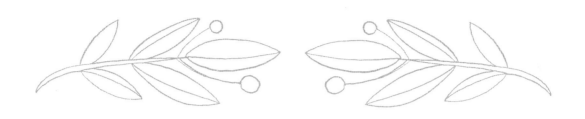

Choose three people who
have not been on your prayer list before.
Pray for them for an entire week.

Pray

don't be afraid, just believe

Mark 5:36

don't be afraid, just believe

Mark 5:36

White lines that emphasize the delicate curves of the birds, leaves, and letters are offset by the strong, dark color of the text.

What are you most afraid of?
How can you move past that fear?

Mark 5:36

Adding a harvest moon behind this sentiment adds
to the autumn vibe of gold, red, and orange.

Why should we gather
before giving thanks?

_____
_____
_____
_____
_____
_____
_____

Thankfulness

for we walk by faith, not by sight.

2 Corinthians 5:7

Choosing the earthy greens, blues, and golds of trees, the sea, and sunshine gives this piece a vivacity corresponding to its message of a living faith.

for we walk by faith, not by sight.

2 Corinthians 5:7

What is a concrete way that you can
walk in faith rather than sight?

2 Corinthians 5:7

start each day with a **grateful heart**

Wind becomes visible with the clever addition of pale lines and swirls around the natural colors of the feathers.

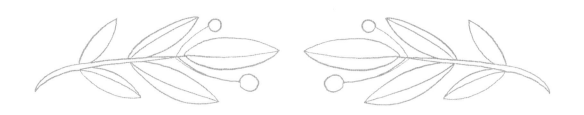

How can you start your day gratefully?
How might it change your day?

Grateful Heart

GOD is Within Her She Will Not fall

psalm 46:5

How can this verse help you
get through your next challenge?

Psalm 46:5

the joy of the LORD is your Strength

Nehemiah 8:10

What is the difference between
joy and happiness?

Nehemiah 8:10

WiSDOM is a tree of life to those who embrace her; happy are those who hold her tightly.

PROVERBS 3:18

What is the difference between
being smart and having wisdom?

Proverbs 3:18

He has made everything beautiful in its time.

Ecclesiastes 3:11

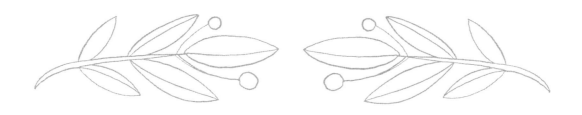

Try to look at an ugly or plain object differently.
How has God made it beautiful?

Ecclesiastes 3:11

I lift up my eyes to
the mountains—
where does my help come from?
My help comes from the Lord,
the Maker of heaven and earth.

Psalm 121:1-2

What are some things you
need to ask for God's help with?

_____
_____
_____
_____
_____
_____
_____

Psalm 121:1-2

"...THOSE WHO KEEP WAITING
FOR THE LORD
WILL RENEW THEIR STRENGTH.
THEN THEY'LL SOAR ON
WINGS LIKE EAGLES..."

ISAIAH 40:31

What does strength look like to you?

Isaiah 40:31

YOU LEAD ME IN THE
path of life;

I EXPERIENCE ABSOLUTE *joy in your presence;*

YOU ALWAYS GIVE ME *sheer delight.*

PSALM 16:11

Whose company makes you truly happy?
Why?

_____

_____

_____

_____

_____

_____

_____

_____

Psalm 16:11

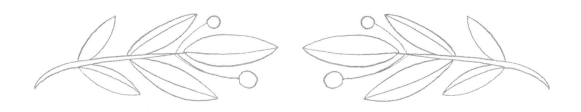

What makes a house a home?

Bless Our Nest

Do unto Others as you would have them do unto you. Matthew 7:12

Think about a recent instance
when you didn't follow the golden rule.
How can you act differently next time?

Matthew 7:12

For where your
Treasure is,

family

there will your
heart be also

Luke 12:34

What are your treasures?
Where is your heart?

Luke 12:34

live in harmony with one another, be Sympathetic, live as brothers, be Compassionate and humble.

1 Peter 3:8

Think of some ways you can facilitate harmony
in your workplace or home.

1 Peter 3:8

She is Clothed in **Strength** and **Dignity** and she **Laughs** without fear of the **Future**

Proverbs 31:25

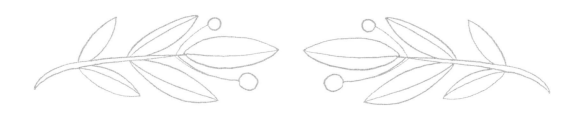

What scares you about the future?
How can you turn that fear into laughter for today?

_____

Proverbs 31:25

whatever one sows,

GALATIANS 6:7

that will he also Reap

How has the idea of reaping what one sows
played out in your life?

_____

_____

_____

_____

_____

_____

Galatians 6:7

BELIEVE

HOPE

PRAY

FORGIVE

COMFORT

LOVE

REJOICE

Glory to God

Cut out or copy these bookmarks.

Use these designs in the corners and margins of your Bible or journal.

Add notes or book names in these boxes and tags.